An atom.

To squash.

Area = Length x Width

100°C

A chemical reaction which breaks down a compound.

... number of protons in 1 atom.

Surrounding the nucleus (in the shell).

The amount of matter in a certain volume (g/cm^3).

0°C.

A chemical reaction.

A liquid.

Negative charge.

Only one type of atom.

The study of matter.

- Bubbles
- Change in temperature
- Colour change
- Change in size

Evaporation.

A combining reaction.

118.

Freezing.

A substance formed when 2 or more elements combine in a chemical reaction.

It increases.

Materials

What is the formula to work out area?

Materials

What does 'to compress' mean?

Materials

What is the smallest part of an element?

Materials

What does the atomic number of an element tell us?

Materials

What is a decomposing reaction?

Materials

What is the normal boiling point of water?

Materials

What is the normal melting point of water?

Materials

What does density mean?

Materials

Where in an atom would you find the electrons?

Materials

What charge do electrons have?

Materials

What does a gas become when it condenses?

Materials

What has to take place in order for a new substance to be formed?

Materials

Give four signs that a chemical reaction has taken place.

Materials

What is chemistry?

Materials

How many different types of atom are there in an element?

Materials

Approximately how many elements are there in the Periodic Table?

Materials

What do we call a chemical reaction which makes a compound?

Materials

Name the physical reaction that takes place when a liquid becomes a gas.

Materials

When an object or substance expands, what happens to its volume?

Materials

What is a compound?

Materials

Name the physical process that takes place when a liquid becomes a solid.

Materials & Their Properties Active Learning Game

Fresh Focus on Learning

Oaka BOOKS

1 START: Place your counters here and roll the dice.

2 ?

3 Atoms are the smallest parts of elements. Go forward 1 space.

4 ?

5 ?

6 Atoms join together to form molecules. Jump 3 spaces.

7 ?

! You mix sugar into tea to make an impure substance. Miss A Go.

8 The gritter lorry puts salt on the road to lower the freezing point of water.

9 ?

10 Fun Fact: You boil a kettle on top of Mount Everest. It boils quickly at just 71°C. Jump 2 spaces.

11 You leave iron out in the rain. The oxygen and water form rust when they react with the iron. Go back to the Start.

12 ?

! You leave a pan to boil. All the liquid evaporates and it boils dry! Miss A Go.

13 You fill a balloon with helium and it floats away! Go back 4 spaces.

14 About 100 elements are listed in Dmitri Mendeleev's table. Name the table to jump 1 space.

15 ?

16 You combine 2 or more elements to make a compound.

17 ?

18 The atomic mass of an element is measured in g.

! You spill a glass of water. The particles in the liquid flow across the table! Miss A Go.

?

20 Gold and silver are used to make jewellery because they are unreactive and can be polished and bent.

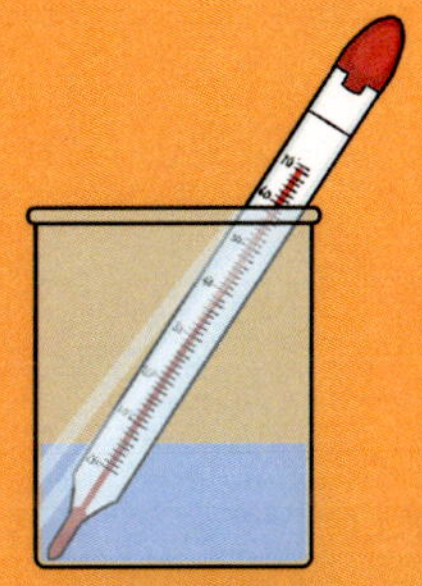

21 ?

22 FINISH

How to play the Materials & Their Properties Active Learning Game:

- Roll the dice to decide who starts (highest roll starts).
- Begin at the Start star and make your way around the board.
- If you land on a ? space, answer the next ? card. If you get the question right, roll the dice again. Get it wrong and you miss a turn.
- The winner is the first person to reach the Moon!

Don't forget, you can also use the Question

Transport & Industry Active Learning Game

Fresh Focus on Learning

Oaka BOOKS

1 START: Place your counters here and roll the dice.

2 ?

3 You buy a new smart phone from a shop. This is part of the service (tertiary) industry.

4 ?

5 ?

6 Your phone was designed in the quaternary industry (full of clever people doing research and development).

7 ?

! You get a bus to the other side of town to meet a mate. Your friend, who lives in the country, is late as there are not many buses! MISS A GO!

8 You go on a trip around a car factory. You see raw materials being turned into car parts. This is the secondary industry in action!

9 ?

10 You take the train from London to Paris (HS1) and arrive in time for lunch. Jump forward 2 spaces.

! A new factory is being built near your school. Parents and teachers are worried about pollution. MISS A GO!

11 ?

12 You are going on a weekend trip to the Isle of Wight but miss the ferry. Go back to the start.

13 A music festival has brought money to the area but locals are worried about noise and rubbish.

14 ?

15 The local farmer is angry that visitors to the festival are walking in his fields! Go back 2 spaces.

16 ?

17 The new signs for the footpaths have helped stop visitors getting lost! Jump forward 1 space.

18 ?

! The local people are worried about pollution and noise from the new airport runway. MISS A GO!

19 A ship carrying containers gets stuck on a sandbank going into the port. The shipping lanes are blocked! Go back 2 spaces.

20 ?

21 FINISH

How to play the Transport & Industry Board Game:

- Roll the dice to decide who starts (highest roll starts).
- Begin at the Start star and make your way around the board.
- If you land on a ? space, answer the next ? card. If you get the question right, roll the dice again. Get it wrong and you miss a turn.
- The winner is the first person to reach the Finish.

Don't forget, you can also use the Question

Weather & Climate Active Learning Game

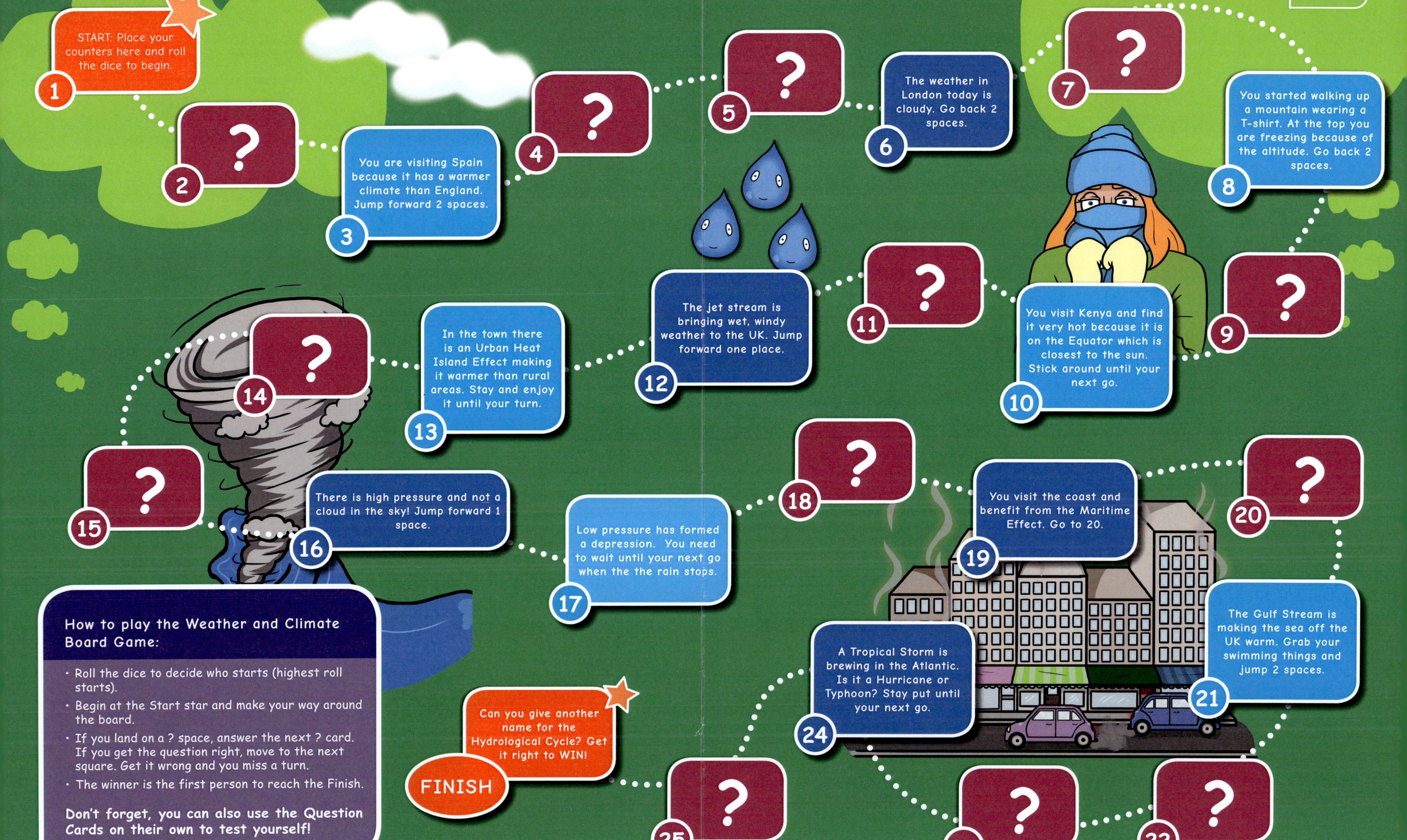

How to play the Weather and Climate Board Game:

- Roll the dice to decide who starts (highest roll starts).
- Begin at the Start star and make your way around the board.
- If you land on a ? space, answer the next ? card. If you get the question right, move to the next square. Get it wrong and you miss a turn.
- The winner is the first person to reach the Finish.

Don't forget, you can also use the Question Cards on their own to test yourself!

Imports

A honeypot site.

To send a product out of a country to be sold in another country.

More Economically Developed Country

Manufacturing

Less Economically Developed Country

A statistic which measures people's ability to buy (or find) enough resources to meet all their needs.

Jobs/activities that get or extract raw materials from the earth or sea.

Newly Industrialised Country.

Subsistence farming.

Jobs/activities that make products from raw materials.

Jobs/activities involved in research and development.

Visual pollution.

Jobs/activities involved in providing a service or selling goods.

An activity that involves the careful use of resources so they can be used by future generations.

- Food production e.g. baker
- Building
- Car manufacturer

- Fishing & farming
- Forestry
- Mining
- Drilling

- Primary
- Secondary
- Tertiary
- Quaternary

- Scientists
- Researchers

Service industry.

- Doctors
- Teachers
- Lawyers

Transport & Industry

What does to 'export' mean?

Transport & Industry

What do we call a site which attracts lots of tourists?

Transport & Industry

What word do we use to describe goods that are brought into a country from another country?

Transport & Industry

What does LEDC stand for?

Transport & Industry

What word do we use to describe making a product in a factory or workshop?

Transport & Industry

What does MEDC stand for?

Transport & Industry

What does NIC stand for?

Transport & Industry

What does 'primary industry' mean?

Transport & Industry

What is meant by the term 'quality of life'?

Transport & Industry

What is meant by the term 'quaternary industry'?

Transport & Industry

What is meant by the term 'secondary industry'?

Transport & Industry

If you are farming to provide food for yourself, what term would we use to describe it?

Transport & Industry

What is meant by the term 'sustainable activity'?

Transport & Industry

What is meant by the term 'tertiary industry'?

Transport & Industry

There are buildings spoiling a view. What type of pollution is this?

Transport & Industry

What are the four main types of industry?

Transport & Industry

Give an example of a primary industry.

Transport & Industry

Give an example of a secondary industry.

Transport & Industry

Give an example of a tertiary job.

Transport & Industry

What is another term we use to describe tertiary industry?

Transport & Industry

Give an example of a quaternary job.

- Where workers live?
- Cost of labour.
- Is there space to build?
- Where is the market?
- Are there leisure activities?
- Are there Government grants?
- Are there transport links?

Quaternary industry.

Primary industry.

- Litter
- Erosion
- Pollution
- Conflict with land owners.
- Dogs chasing farm animals.

- Pesticides can kill wildlife.
- Fertilisers can pollute rivers.
- Destroy habitats.
- Visual & noise pollution.
- Smells from slurry and animals.

- Landscape.
- Atmosphere of an area.
- Habitat for plants and animals.

- Removal of trees can cause erosion.
- Natural habitat changed.
- Noise pollution from machinery.

- Noise pollution.
- Visual pollution from factories.
- CO_2 pollution from factories and transport.

- Visual pollution.
- Dust and noise pollution.
- Habitats destroyed.

- Plant flowers to attract wildlife.
- Replant hedges.
- Don't use chemicals.

- Minimise CO_2 emissions.
- Use renewable energy.
- Reduce waste.
- Recycle.

The careful use of resources so they are maintained for the future.

\+ Convenient.
\+ Shorter journey times.
\- Pollution.
\- Cost.
\- Noise.
\- Destroy environment to make new roads.

- Brings money to local economy.
- Can cause damage to environment.

- Reduce trampling of crops.
- Reduce erosion.
- Easy for tourists to follow.

\+ Quick.
\+ Safer than road or rail.
\+ Good for light goods.
\- Expensive.
\- CO_2 pollution.
\- Noise pollution.
\- Need other transport to get to airport.

\+ Can carry goods over long distance cheaply.
\- Takes a long time.

\+ Carry large amounts of freight.
\+ Less CO_2 per person than road transport.
\- Can be expensive.
\- Noise pollution.
\- Destroys habitats.

Transnational Corporation

The process by which the world is becoming more connected through trade and cultural exchange.

- Getting to work.
- Getting to school.
- Getting into towns.
- Leisure, tourism, socialising.
- To move goods around.

Transport & Industry

Fresh Focus on Learning Oaka BOOKS

In LEDC countries, which type of industry has the most workers?

Transport & Industry

Fresh Focus on Learning Oaka BOOKS

In MEDC countries, which type of industry is the fastest growing?

Transport & Industry

Fresh Focus on Learning Oaka BOOKS

Give 3 things that companies have to think about for the location of businesses.

Transport & Industry

Fresh Focus on Learning Oaka BOOKS

Which 3 things make up the environment?

Transport & Industry

Fresh Focus on Learning Oaka BOOKS

Give 3 negative effects of farming on an area.

Transport & Industry

Designed for dyslexics, effective for everyone Oaka BOOKS

Give 3 negative effects of tourism on an area.

Transport & Industry

Fresh Focus on Learning Oaka BOOKS

Give 3 negative effects of mining on an area.

Transport & Industry

Designed for dyslexics, effective for everyone Oaka BOOKS

Give 3 negative effects of industry on an area.

Transport & Industry

Fresh Focus on Learning Oaka BOOKS

How can forestry negatively affect an area?

Transport & Industry

Fresh Focus on Learning Oaka BOOKS

What does the term 'stewardship' mean?

Transport & Industry

Fresh Focus on Learning Oaka BOOKS

Give 3 ways in which factories can make their economic development sustainable.

Transport & Industry

Fresh Focus on Learning Oaka BOOKS

Give 3 ways in which farmers can make their economic development sustainable.

Transport & Industry

Fresh Focus on Learning Oaka BOOKS

Why are clearly marked footpaths good for the environment?

Transport & Industry

Fresh Focus on Learning Oaka BOOKS

Give one positive and one negative effect of tourism on an area.

Transport & Industry

Fresh Focus on Learning Oaka BOOKS

Give one positive and one negative effect of travelling by car.

Transport & Industry

Fresh Focus on Learning Oaka BOOKS

Give one positive and one negative effect of travelling by rail.

Transport & Industry

Fresh Focus on Learning Oaka BOOKS

Give one positive and one negative effect of transporting goods by ship.

Transport & Industry

Fresh Focus on Learning Oaka BOOKS

Give one positive and one negative effect of travelling by air.

Transport & Industry

Fresh Focus on Learning Oaka BOOKS

Give 3 reasons why good transport routes are important.

Transport & Industry

Fresh Focus on Learning Oaka BOOKS

What does 'globalisation' mean?

Transport & Industry

Fresh Focus on Learning Oaka BOOKS

What is a 'TNC'?

Fresh Focus on Learning

Instructions for Teachers and Parents

Oaka™ Books Topic Packs help children learn in three different ways. Use the pack in the following order to help your child or pupil understand and retain the information better.

1. Read the Topic Booklet:

The Topic Booklet gives the key facts laid out in an accessible way for all children, whatever their ability. Some children will be able to read and understand this booklet working on their own. Each section is short and concise, enabling children to participate even if their reading is weak and they require some degree of help.

2. Interact with the Active Learning Map or Game:

Depending on the Topic Pack, your pack will contain EITHER*:

- An Active Learning Game with Question & Answer flashcards

OR

- An Active Learning Map with Character cards.

*The active learning activity will vary depending on the Topic Pack.

For Active Learning Maps:
Follow the instructions given on the Active Learning Map. There are questions around the map to act as prompts for your child or pupils. Use the Character cards to either match up with the questions or to position the characters in the right place on the map in order to tell the story of the events. Use the map and characters as creatively as you can to tell their story.

Adding silly accents and rhymes will help your child/pupils really engage with the topic and remember the information. This is an ideal activity for small groups of up to 4 players and helps make learning some facts fun! Repeating the game regularly will help children retain the information.

For Active Learning Games:
Follow the instructions given on the game sheet. The game comes with a set of Question and Answer flashcards to be answered when you land on a ? space.

These cards can also be used independently as a Quick Quiz for revision. Again, this is an ideal activity for small groups for up to 4 players and helps make learning some facts fun! Repeating the game regularly will help children to retain the information.

3. Write Your Own Notes:

See how much your child/pupil can recall by working through the Write Your Own Notes Booklet. This will require them to re0read the information and complete the blanks or write their own notes on the topic, recalling as much from memory as possible. They should use the Topic Booklet if they get stuck.

The Write Your Own Notes Booklet follows the same format as the Topic Booklet, giving a visual prompt with the illustrations. The numbered sections make it easy to find information in the Topic Booklet if they need a little extra help.

If you require any further help or have any suggestions as to how this Topic Pack can be improved, please email us at info@oakabooks.co.uk. Thank you.

- Altitude
- Latitude
- Distance from sea
- Prevailing winds
- Wind Belts

Weather is the condition of the atmosphere at a certain time or place.

Climate is the average weather in a place over a period of time.

Because the sea does not heat up and cool down as quickly as land does.

As altitude increases, temperature decreases.

Altitude is the height above sea level.

There are 6 wind belts.

Latitude is the distance a place is from the Equator.

The Equator.

Climate in N.W of the UK:
Cool summers, mild winters, heavy rain all year.

The prevailing wind is the usual direction of the wind in a place.

Wind belts affect temperature and rainfall.

Climate in N.E of UK:
Cool summers, cold winters, steady rain all year.

A climate graph shows temperature and rainfall over a period of time.

The prevailing wind affects temperature and rainfall.

Climate in S.W. of UK:
Warm summers, mild winters, light rain all year especially in winter.

A microclimate is where there are very local differences in the climate of a place.

A microclimate.

Climate in S.E.of U.K:
Warm summers,
mild wint

- buildings and roads radiate heat
- pollution causes a Greenhouse effect
- pollution stops the sun
- tall buildings can stop the wind

The Urban Heat Effect.

Weather

What is climate?

Weather

What is weather?

Weather

What are the 5 factors that affect climate?

Weather

What is altitude?

Weather

What happens to the temperature as the altitude increases?

Weather

Why is the temperature range less the closer you are to the sea?

Weather

What is the name of the line that goes around the centre of the Earth from West to East?

Weather

What does latitude tell us?

Weather

How many wind belts are there?

Weather

What do wind belts affect?

Weather

What is the prevailing wind?

Weather

Can you summarise the climate in the North West of the UK?

Weather

Which two things does the prevailing wind affect?

Weather

What does a climate graph show?

Weather

Can you summarise the climate in the North East of the UK?

Weather

What is the name given to very local differences in the climate of a place?

Weather

Can you explain what a Microclimate is?

Weather

Can you summarise the climate in the South West of the UK?

Weather

In a town the average temperature is higher than in a rural area. What is this called?

Weather

Can you give 2 reasons why towns are generally warmer than rural areas?

Weather

Can you summarise the climate in the North East of the UK?

A barometer.	To keep it out of direct sunlight.	· Temperature · Air pressure · Wind · Precipitation (or humidity) · Clouds (or amount of sun)
High pressure.	It condenses.	A depression.
Precipitation.	A wind vane.	An anemometer.
· Relief rainfall · Convectional rainfall · Frontal rainfall	A rain gauge.	Water droplets.
The rain shadow.	Convectional rainfall.	Relief rainfall.
A warm current in the sea from the Gulf of Mexico to Europe.	Frontal rainfall.	A weather front.
So we can prepare and plan.	Isobars.	A weather expert.

Weather Fresh Focus on Learning Oaka BOOKS

What 5 things affect the weather?

Weather Fresh Focus on Learning Oaka BOOKS

Why is a thermometer kept in a Stephenson Box?

Weather Fresh Focus on Learning Oaka BOOKS

What is used to measure air pressure?

Weather Fresh Focus on Learning Oaka BOOKS

What is another name for an area of low pressure?

Weather Fresh Focus on Learning Oaka BOOKS

When air rises, what physical change happens to it to form clouds?

Weather Fresh Focus on Learning Oaka BOOKS

If there are clear skies and calm weather, is it an area of high or low pressure?

Weather Fresh Focus on Learning Oaka BOOKS

What equipment is used to measure wind speed?

Weather Fresh Focus on Learning Oaka BOOKS

What equipment is used to tell the direction of the wind?

Weather Fresh Focus on Learning Oaka BOOKS

What is the proper name for the water which falls from the sky?

Weather Fresh Focus on Learning Oaka BOOKS

What are clouds formed from?

Weather Fresh Focus on Learning Oaka BOOKS

What is used to collect and measure rainfall?

Weather Fresh Focus on Learning Oaka BOOKS

What are the three types of rainfall?

Weather Fresh Focus on Learning Oaka BOOKS

Which type of rainfall happens when warm, wet winds climb a hill?

Weather Fresh Focus on Learning Oaka BOOKS

Which type of rainfall happens in very hot areas?

Weather Fresh Focus on Learning Oaka BOOKS

When it is raining on one side of a hill, what is the dry area on the other side called?

Weather Fresh Focus on Learning Oaka BOOKS

What do we call the line where two air masses of different temperatures meet?

Weather Fresh Focus on Learning Oaka BOOKS

What type of rainfall is caused when warm air meets cold air?

Weather Fresh Focus on Learning Oaka BOOKS

What is the Gulf Stream?

Weather Fresh Focus on Learning Oaka BOOKS

What is a meteorologist?

Weather Fresh Focus on Learning Oaka BOOKS

What are the circles showing areas of pressure on weather maps called?

Weather Fresh Focus on Learning Oaka BOOKS

Why do we need to be able to forecast big storms?

Typhoons.

Hurricanes.

Areas of very low pressure.

They can be anything from a few metres wide up to the largest recorded one of 4.2m (Oklahoma 2013).

A tornado.

Warm seas.

The loss of water from plants back into the air. It happens through diffusion and evaporation.

Some of it evaporates.

The Water Cycle.

Arctic Wind.

Overland flow.

When water flows through permeable rocks and soil.

Heavy rain.

Relief rainfall.

The Gulf Stream.

Rain.

Because warm air is lighter.

Convectional rainfall.

The south-east.

Because they are the furthest points from the Equator.

A climate graph.

Weather

Fresh Focus on Learning Oaka Books

Are tropical storms areas of very low or very high pressure?

Weather

What do we call tropical storms in the Atlantic Ocean?

Weather

What do we call tropical storms in the Pacific Ocean?

Weather

What does a hurricane need in order to form?

Weather

What do we call a violent, spinning column of air?

Weather

How wide are tornadoes?

Weather

What is another name for the Hydrological Cycle?

Weather

What happens to water from the sea or lakes when it is heated by the Sun?

Weather

What is transpiration?

Weather

What is percolation?

Weather

What do we call the water that runs over very wet land?

Weather

What is the cold wind that blows towards the north-east of England?

Weather

What helps keep the seas around the UK mild in temperature?

Weather

What type of rainfall occurs in the north-west of England?

Weather

Is convectional rainfall usually light rain or heavy rain?

Weather

What type of rainfall do we only get in the UK when it is very hot?

Weather

Why does warm air rise over cold air?

Weather

If the prevailing wind comes across water, what will it bring with it?

Weather

What type of chart would you use to show temperature and rainfall?

Weather

Why is it coldest at both the North and South poles?

Weather

Which area of the UK has the better weather?

Fresh Focus on Learning

Instructions for Teachers and Parents

Oaka™ Books Topic Packs help children learn in three different ways. Use the pack in the following order to help your child or pupil understand and retain the information better.

1. Read the Topic Booklet:

The Topic Booklet gives the key facts laid out in an accessible way for all children, whatever their ability. Some children will be able to read and understand this booklet working on their own. Each section is short and concise, enabling children to participate even if their reading is weak and they require some degree of help.

2. Interact with the Active Learning Map or Game:

Depending on the Topic Pack, your pack will contain EITHER*:

- An Active Learning Game with Question & Answer flashcards

OR

- An Active Learning Map with Character cards.

*The active learning activity will vary depending on the Topic Pack.

For Active Learning Maps:
Follow the instructions given on the Active Learning Map. There are questions around the map to act as prompts for your child or pupils. Use the Character cards to either match up with the questions or to position the characters in the right place on the map in order to tell the story of the events. Use the map and characters as creatively as you can to tell their story.

Adding silly accents and rhymes will help your child/pupils really engage with the topic and remember the information. This is an ideal activity for small groups of up to 4 players and helps make learning some facts fun! Repeating the game regularly will help children retain the information.

For Active Learning Games:
Follow the instructions given on the game sheet. The game comes with a set of Question and Answer flashcards to be answered when you land on a ? space.

These cards can also be used independently as a Quick Quiz for revision. Again, this is an ideal activity for small groups for up to 4 players and helps make learning some facts fun! Repeating the game regularly will help children to retain the information.

3. Write Your Own Notes:

See how much your child/pupil can recall by working through the Write Your Own Notes Booklet. This will require them to re0read the information and complete the blanks or write their own notes on the topic, recalling as much from memory as possible. They should use the Topic Booklet if they get stuck.

The Write Your Own Notes Booklet follows the same format as the Topic Booklet, giving a visual prompt with the illustrations. The numbered sections make it easy to find information in the Topic Booklet if they need a little extra help.

If you require any further help or have any suggestions as to how this Topic Pack can be improved, please email us at info@oakabooks.co.uk. Thank you.

· Close together.
· Randomly arranged.
· Flowing.
· Cannot be squashed.

· Regular pattern.
· Close together.
· Cannot be squashed.

A substance made of 2 or more elements or compounds.

Melting.

The Periodic Table.

· Randomly arranged.
· Moving around.
· Fill the space.
· Can be squashed.

Positive.

In the nucleus of an atom.

A mixture.

In the nucleus.

Protons and Neutrons in the nucleus.

One made from just one type of element or compound.

Sublimation.

Solid, liquid, gas.

No charge.

The Mass Number.

A molecule.

Volume = Length x Width x Height.

Because there are spaces between the molecules.

Nothing at all! The chemical structure will stay the same.

Reactants are the substances you start with. Products are the substances you end up with.

Materials

What is an impure substance?

Materials

How are the particles in a solid arranged?

Materials

How are the particles in a liquid arranged?

Materials

How are the particles in a gas arranged?

Materials

What is the name of the table of elements created by Dmitri Mendeleev?

Materials

Name the physical change which happens when a solid becomes a liquid?

Materials

What name to we give to 2 or more substances mixed together with no chemical reaction taking place?

Materials

Where are protons found?

Materials

What charge do protons have?

Materials

What is a pure substance?

Materials

What part of an atom gives it it's mass?

Materials

Where in an atom is a neutron found?

Materials

What charge does a neutron have?

Materials

What are the 3 basic states of matter?

Materials

What do we call the physical change when a substance turns from solid to gas?

Materials

What formula would you use to work out the volume of a box?

Materials

When 2 or more atoms bond, what do they form?

Materials

The number of protons AND neutrons in an atom is called what?

Materials

What are the reactants and products in a chemical reaction?

Materials

During a physical change, what will happen to the chemical structure of a substance?

Materials

Why can gas be compressed?

Instructions for Teachers and Parents

Oaka™ Books Topic Packs help children learn in three different ways. Use the pack in the following order to help your child or pupil understand and retain the information better.

1. Read the Topic Booklet:

The Topic Booklet gives the key facts laid out in an accessible way for all children, whatever their ability. Some children will be able to read and understand this booklet working on their own. Each section is short and concise, enabling children to participate even if their reading is weak and they require some degree of help.

2. Interact with the Active Learning Map or Game:

Depending on the Topic Pack, your pack will contain EITHER*:

- An Active Learning Game with Question & Answer flashcards

OR

- An Active Learning Map with Character cards.

*The active learning activity will vary depending on the Topic Pack.

For Active Learning Maps:
Follow the instructions given on the Active Learning Map. There are questions around the map to act as prompts for your child or pupils. Use the Character cards to either match up with the questions or to position the characters in the right place on the map in order to tell the story of the events. Use the map and characters as creatively as you can to tell their story.

Adding silly accents and rhymes will help your child/pupils really engage with the topic and remember the information. This is an ideal activity for small groups of up to 4 players and helps make learning some facts fun! Repeating the game regularly will help children retain the information.

For Active Learning Games:
Follow the instructions given on the game sheet. The game comes with a set of Question and Answer flashcards to be answered when you land on a ? space.

These cards can also be used independently as a Quick Quiz for revision. Again, this is an ideal activity for small groups for up to 4 players and helps make learning some facts fun! Repeating the game regularly will help children to retain the information.

3. Write Your Own Notes:

See how much your child/pupil can recall by working through the Write Your Own Notes Booklet. This will require them to reOread the information and complete the blanks or write their own notes on the topic, recalling as much from memory as possible. They should use the Topic Booklet if they get stuck.

The Write Your Own Notes Booklet follows the same format as the Topic Booklet, giving a visual prompt with the illustrations. The numbered sections make it easy to find information in the Topic Booklet if they need a little extra help.

If you require any further help or have any suggestions as to how this Topic Pack can be improved, please email us at info@oakabooks.co.uk. Thank you.